Ruthie - with
love - Tina. May '76.

The
Death of a Wombat

The Death of

With paintings, etchings and line drawings

a Wombat

Ivan Smith
by Clifton Pugh

 wren

WREN PUBLISHING PTY LTD
33 Lonsdale Street, Melbourne

© Text: Ivan Smith 1972
© Paintings, etchings and line drawings: Clifton Pugh 1972

National Library of Australia Card Service Number
and ISBN 0 85885 009 5
Registered in Australia for transmission by post as a book
Text set by Trade Composition Pty Ltd, Melbourne
Printed and bound by Wilke and Company Limited,
Clayton, Victoria
Designed by Derrick I. Stone

Acknowledgements
The publisher wishes to thank the Australian
Broadcasting Commission for releasing the publishing rights
of *The Death of a Wombat* which was originally a
Radio Documentary, written by Ivan Smith, with music
composed by George English, and which won the Prix
Italia Competition in 1959.

Foreword
H.R.H. The Duke of Edinburgh

 BUCKINGHAM PALACE

Nature affects people in many different ways, and attitudes to nature can vary from total ignorance and indifference to total obsession. It is almost impossible for us to be objective about nature because we are part of it. We are animate while all our splendid creations, whether they are the products of artistic or engineering genius, are inanimate, dead, lifeless. We have more in common with any living creature than with the best of our more familiar mechanical companions, such as motor cars or television sets.

I rather suspect that it is this recognition of the relationship between men and animals which is at the bottom of the anthropomorphic attitude; the giving of human qualities to animals. Whatever may be the reason, there is a long history of extremely popular illustrated stories about humanized animals. They may not represent reality but they make a deep and lasting impression.

The Death of a Wombat is in this tradition and it is obviously a brilliant combination of artistic and literary talent. The result is a deeply moving document.

1972

PRESIDENT, AUSTRALIAN CONSERVATION FOUNDATION

Author's Introduction:

My first meeting with the Australian wombat was a very happy one. For me it was gratitude at first sight. It came about by way of a postcard, which I happened to see on a rack in my local newsagency. I bought three copies, forgot what else it was I had been wanting, and walked into a little park to study every detail.

There was minimal information on the back of the card: 'Australian native animals. The wombat – a burrowing, herbivorous, nocturnal marsupial.' It was little to go on, but I was sure he was what I had been looking for for weeks.

I had been wanting to write a sort of allegory on the human condition as I had been seeing it as a young man. I wanted to synthesise certain groups of human characteristics, and to set these groups in contrast in order to say something about human success and failure. I couldn't find a mould for it, and so I couldn't even begin to write.
The postcard changed that.

The wombat seemed to be friendly, stupid, innocent, slow – all characteristics that I was looking for in the main figure. I read some books about him, hoping hard that he didn't have one or two highly unpleasant aspects to his character. He hadn't. He had courage, and a certain amount of resourcefulness and doggedness. The only drawback was that he was nocturnal, but that could easily be ignored.

I read through biologies of other outback animals and found all I wanted.
The kangaroo – strong, tough, but too stupid to win through in a calamity.
The koala – decent enough, but unimaginative and unenterprising, among the first types to go under in country-wide adversity.
The dingo – tough, resilient, and with the cunning that sees people through when times are out of joint.
The wombat – with the sort of gentleness and vulnerability that make nice guys finish last.

My reading led me to think that a bushfire would provide a suitable social disaster common to the fates of these animal symbols.

Like the great majority of Australians I have always been a big-city dweller, and my knowledge of bushfires had been confined to black-and-white newsfilm. Detailed descriptions of them gave me a forcible impression of their ugly ruthlessness. So thankfully, I was on my way; I could start to write.

The *Death of a Wombat* has now been broadcast in several countries, and I have been very interested in individual reactions to it. An American friend asked me if I saw something of the dingo in the late President John Kennedy. An Englishman said he saw something of the wombat in W. H. Auden. It might be better not to mention some names that have been linked with the kangaroo and the koala.

What is heartening to me these days is that, although many people realise that the wombat has a hard time of it in our society, and generally goes under in any social turbulence, he nevertheless represents what is widely held to be worthwhile, and even admirable.

Artist's Introduction:

The artificiality and sophistication of city life has always irked me.
This, coupled with an urgent need to come closer, to become more at
one with my landscape subjects, eventually led me to move out of
Melbourne and to establish at Cottle's Bridge, Victoria, in collaboration
with other painters and potters, a co-operative to protect the
environment.

As I became more and more involved with nature, I found suddenly
in myself a growing awareness of and concern with the problems of
animal conservation.

It was about this time I first heard the radio broadcast of Ivan Smith's
The Death of a Wombat. It is difficult to describe how much this work
impressed me. The writer seemed to share the view of nature that I tried
to portray through my canvases – nature raw and untamed, and yet
infinitely beautiful; nature: a personality, a force, a lover, a killer.
If I, as the critics have said, embody my landscapes with human
emotions, so too had Ivan Smith in his vivid and moving word pictures.

Like this writer, my love of nature is completely uncritical. On my
property, I steep myself in it, surround myself with its subjects.
The animals who share my property: the kangaroos Flopsy, Kangi
and Rudi, the emus and cockatoos, the wombats we have reared, they
have long been my models, my inspiration and my companions.

So, when the publisher first approached me and asked me to paint and
draw to *The Death of a Wombat*, I agreed, for the form and content of
each canvas was already clear in my mind . . . indeed I was eager to begin.

Here was my opportunity to portray nature in its varying moods,
within a single theme.

And no less importantly, it gave me an opportunity to dedicate
my share in the creation of this book – to Judith, my wife, who reared
my main model for *The Death of a Wombat*, a helpless, hairless and
blind little handful of wombat which needed feeding with an eye
dropper every two hours, day and night, until we could train it to feed
on its own; to Crump, our first wombat, named in affection for the
wombat who dies in *The Death of a Wombat*; . . . and in so doing,
to make a plea for the conservation and protection of our native
animals and the bushland that is their home.

It is night.
The moon is there.
The story begins in dry bushland,
bristling from the rough skin of Australia.

Not much thunder is heard in the inland
of Australia. Around the coastline it is heard,
when water, hugging the earth,
sends on its moon-drawn tides to crash against the land,
beating against the thrust-up arms of rock;

SEASCAPE
Gouache   20 x 28½ ins

and the crushed–up foam of breakers
races to the beaches like a
horde of angry rats.

But in the inland there is not much thunder. Sometimes there is the distant rumble of massed kangaroos in flight. Sometimes there is the fierce night-dancing of forgotten men. Almost always there is silence, and there is silence now, and briefly the bland and stupefying moon eases the land of the torment of the drought.

The days are dry and hard, and the animals suffer.

But now, for a few hours, snakes are loosely coiled,

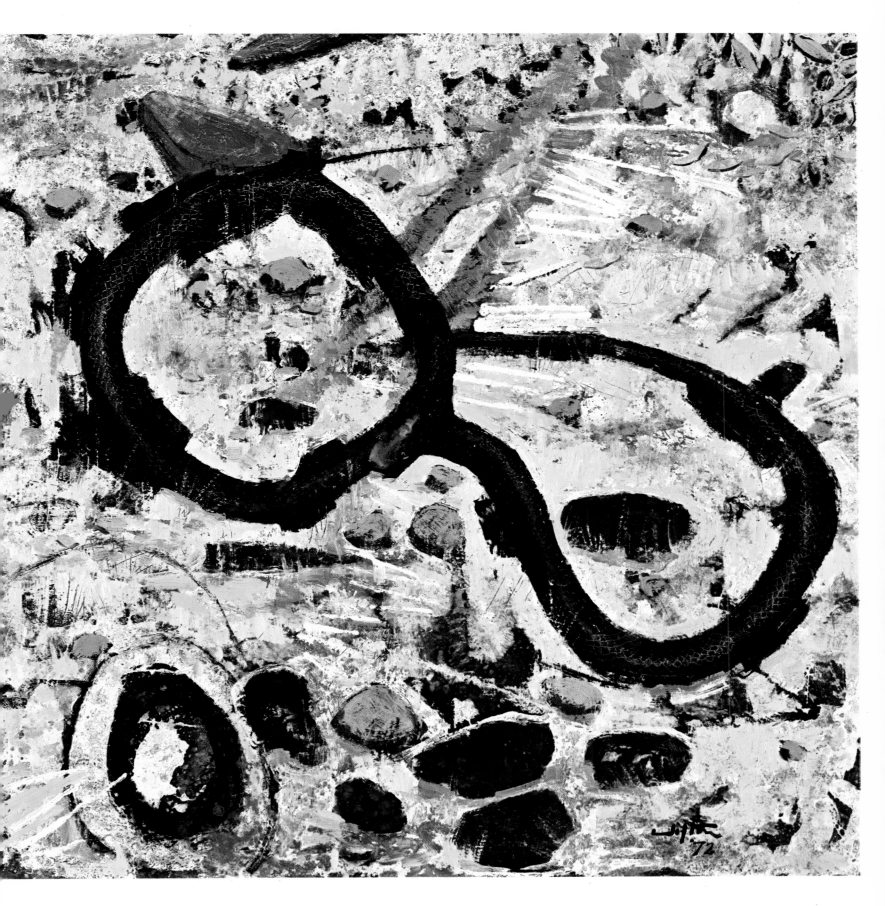

THE PRESENCE OF A SNAKE
Oil   36 x 36 ins

wombats sleep in their holes,

birds' beaks sag in the trees,
and the
flies are still.

WAITING
Oil   36 x 48 ins

A road runs through this part of the country. Near it is the quiet preparation for another sort of thunder. A bottle lies here, brown, unbroken. Tomorrow it will bend thirty square inches of summer sunlight into five. This will go on for some hours. Before noon, more than twelve hundred square miles of bushland will be totally destroyed.

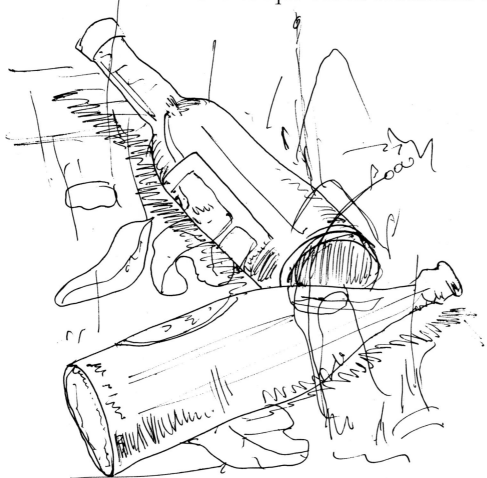

WIDE LANDSCAPE
Gouache   22½ x 30 ins

But, for the time,
the flies sleep,

NUPTIAL FLIGHT OF THE BUTTERFLIES
Oil   36 x 48 ins

the birds are cool,
and the wombats are dozing heaps
in their holes.

Working Drawing.   "Death

"Wombat" ⟨signature⟩ 1972

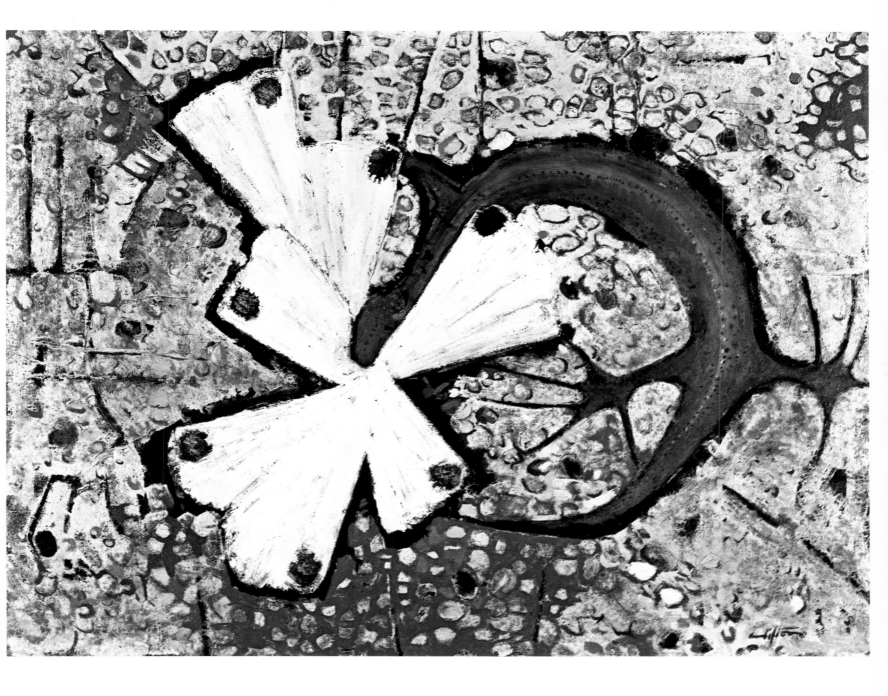

LIZARD AND BUTTERFLY
Oil   36 x 48 ins

Now the dawn . . .
the beginning again . . .
the Australian bush–dawn . . .
the quietest pageant of the earth!

The sun, not yet seen, begins to sketch designs of rock and hill. A silver edging slowly marks out sacs and rims of cloud.

THE DAWN
Indian Ink   16½ x 20 ins

The tips of trees
begin the day's thinking
while their roots
still lie asleep.

THE DAY'S THINKING BEGINS
Oil   48 x 71 ins

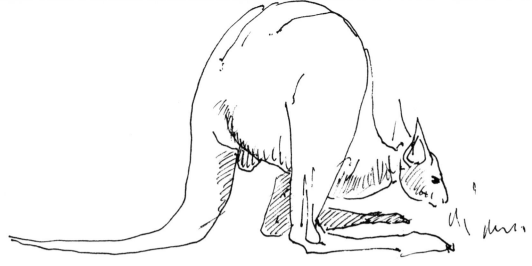

The first bird calls are over.
The crest of a ridge grows sharp,
and the side in darkness for a time grows darker. The air
becomes warmer with every minute. In a paddock sheep
have woken and are standing, moving slowly over
their land as the foam of calm water might move over
rocks and sand-bars.

APOSTLE BIRDS
Oil   36 x 48 ins

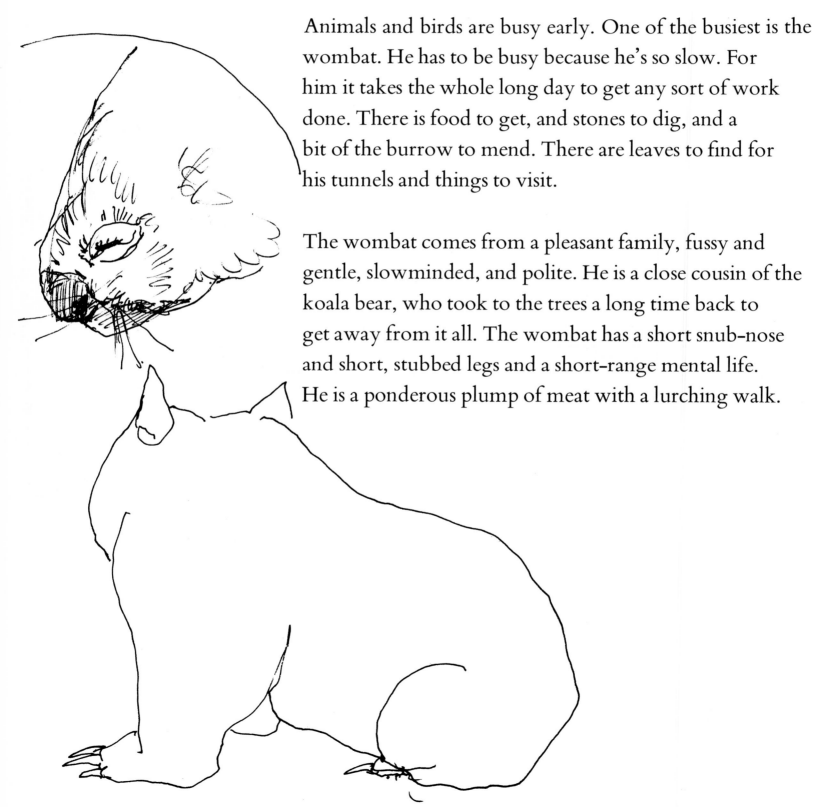

Animals and birds are busy early. One of the busiest is the
wombat. He has to be busy because he's so slow. For
him it takes the whole long day to get any sort of work
done. There is food to get, and stones to dig, and a
bit of the burrow to mend. There are leaves to find for
his tunnels and things to visit.

The wombat comes from a pleasant family, fussy and
gentle, slowminded, and polite. He is a close cousin of the
koala bear, who took to the trees a long time back to
get away from it all. The wombat has a short snub-nose
and short, stubbed legs and a short-range mental life.
He is a ponderous plump of meat with a lurching walk.

SUMMER OF A WOMBAT
Oil   36 x 48 ins

Everything likes a waddler. The wombat lurches on, slowly minding his own business. There are bits of bark to find, and things to visit. And everything likes a waddle and crump, and slowly home to dinner on time, and gentle doze in a well-made hole, and early thoughtless yawns, and waddle and crump again.

If an animal's walk could suggest any words, they
might be these:
'I'm good morning to everything!
Isn't it nice familiar earth!
I'm waddling on and I like to crump.
I'm a ponderous plump of meat and that suits me.
I'm a waddler and slow, and I'm timid and stupid.
I waddle on,
and I waddle slow,
and even waddling nowhere, I still like waddling on.'
It's good that the bush is kind to the wombat.

The trundling snout is pushed along by the high,
ungainly rump. From a wombat's snout-view, the world
perhaps seems strange. But nothing would want to
hurt him. The wombat has no enemy.

He gathers up a bit of bark, and a kangaroo jumps by.
The kangaroo . . . grotesque, fierce, tender, graceful . . .
with the whip-strong paws which fling the small and
delicate face upwards through the air in splendid arcs.
The great prongs of paws bend and crash their downward
thrust at the end of every curve. In the eyes of the tiny,
soaring head there is the fixedness of distance, and behind
the eyes lies an old, old knowledge of an antique land.
The wombat looks at him leap and blinks his eyes.

The wombat almost stumbles over a brown, round thing of glass. That's what comes of trying to think, and letting the waddle and crump take care of itself.

The big rump tumbles from side to side as he goes along to find more bark. Unconcerned, the friend of all the bush moves away from the prism of glass that will lead to the killing of almost every living thing in the bush before twelve o'clock.

The sun pours on to the bottle near the road.

Half-past eight.
The curve of the glass
bends the light to a slim, searing line across the dry leaves underneath. The edges of the leaves begin to curl.

On the way back to his hole, the wombat hears a
muttering in the trees. He is waddling underneath koala
cousin, who sits and nibbles a gum tip on a branch.
Not many koalas left now, because drought has stifled the
gum tips that keep the koala alive.
There are many small bears
dead on the ground.
The wombat surely likes koalas,
furry and round, with flat,
painted noses, as inoffensive
as himself.

Half-past nine.

The jagged leaf-edges blacken.
Steadily the sunlight curves to its scythe-edge,
one foot long.

At the edge of his hole, the wombat lurches over a brown
bush snake. The snake, knowing perhaps that the
wombat's eyesight is not very good, slithers himself away.
Everything likes a waddler.

Ten o'clock.

The base of the bottle cracks off
with a sharp, small explosion.
A brief flicker of flame.

ETCHING. STATE I
Etching   10 x 13¾ ins

The wombat trundles the sand away, using his nose as a spade. Then he lies on his side to dig, and mends his burrow. He makes a much better job of it than the impatient rabbit.

Half-past ten.

A puddle of fire spreads around the bottle.
The glass shatters.

The wombat does not keep
any sort of lookout.
He has no enemies.
Only an inexperienced
dingo might attack him.

DINGO
Oil   36 x 48 ins

The wombat can hurt the dingo.
He backs into a fight,
and the dingo learns that teeth
have no effect on thick, fat-encrusted hide.
The wombat waits till the
moment comes to thrust
his fat rump up and backwards,
cracking the dingo's skull
against a log or a stump.

A quarter-to eleven.

A flashing of a wagtail in the air.
The wombat grunts, and the wagtail carries off his small
beakful of fur. The wombat does not mind, and he backs
himself against his tunnel wall to press the sand down.
Then he is off with waddle and crump to find a stone.

TWO WAGTAILS AND A WOMBAT
Oil   36 x 48 ins

The thunder has begun !

A eucalypt explodes
and there is the first temple of flame.
Flames spread through the undergrowth and send up
blossoms of fine ash. On a distant farm, cocks crow at
mid-day. The roaring startles rabbits, and they scamper
to their burrows.

The flames lash out at neighbouring
trees like the tails of angry cats. A mushroom of muddy
smoke covers the sky. The sun is a far-off scarlet disc.
Scalding sap splinters bark-casings.

A short, round thing of glass has woken the terror of the
ages.

Eleven o'clock,

and it is one long bellow of fire!

The snake that let the wombat go makes hysterical
whip-lash patterns in the air, and hisses out his life.

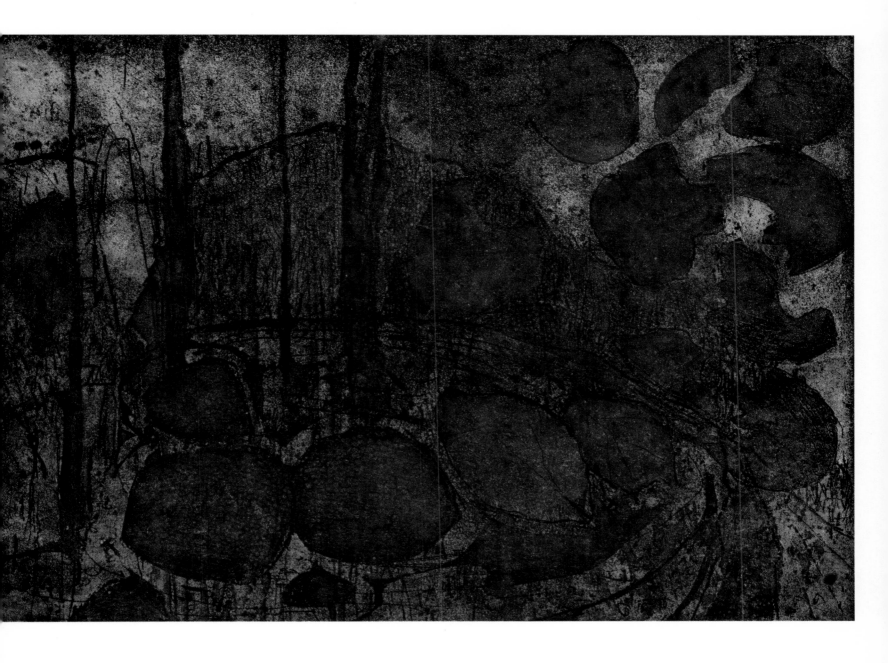

ETCHING. STATE 2
Etching   10 x 13¾ ins

The dingo, cunning and unconquerable, unconquerable
through his cunning, turns to watch the screaming dance
of the approaching fire. The tutorship of his line of sires,
and of his own experience, crowds forward in his mind.
The dingo is the knotting up of nature into a cord of
hard, unfraying toughness. He is savage. He is resolution
without concession. He is animal that masters. He is
ruthlessness, courage and majesty. The dingo stands.
He pants easily now, and waits. He saves his breath and his
blood. He alone has a chance to live. The long, old
knowledge of his line of sires moves into the strong,
spread paws and the heavy-muscled jaws.
He must race through the fire!

Others will race away from it, turn from it. The wombat, cut off from his burrows, will try to reach the only river left with water by the drought. The koala cannot escape. He will, of course, fight for life in the prison to which he has committed himself, the trees that grow the only food that he can live by. The kangaroo may have a better chance. His huge legs might be faster than the fire. Even if the wombat turned, went through the fire, he still might be too slow, and the wombat is very slow. But the dingo has a chance, and he lies down now as the fire approaches, flops on his chest and splays out his paws, and pants very easily to save his heart. He closes his eyes and listens to the flames. The marvellous fine mesh of muscle at the root of either ear manipulates the pointed shapes with delicate precision. In perhaps three minutes his contest will come.

There is a waddle and half a crump. The wombat stops
and stares at a tree. There is a sound in his ears that he has
heard before. Something is wrong. A dingo canters past
and he has his mouth shut. And where have the rabbits
gone? They are always flying in and around the bushes,
but not now. The kangaroos seem to be bounding to
a gathering somewhere behind him. The air has grown
warmer and he has heard this noise before. Go back
to the burrows. Crouching without a sound in the
burrows he has tunnelled into the earth is safety. But his
burrows are there, where the noise is! Noise . . . and
the air getting hot . . . and the animals gone!

The blaze has blackened eighty yards of land. In the next hour it will burn out twenty miles. It is not a fast fire yet . . . twenty miles an hour, but it is too fast for many of the beings of the bush. For the wombat, half a mile in an hour, it is much too fast.

The wombat pushes up his head. Smoke chokes his nostrils. With waddle and crump he moves ten paces on. Still there is smoke. His short snub-nose is damp as the smoke strains out his tear-ducts to protect his eyes.

The river is half a mile away, and his instincts tell him:
there! With waddle and crump and lurching on he begins
to see it, twisted through the shimmer of smoke and tears.
It is very much hotter now but the lurching cannot be
faster. The rump, so much higher than the trundling,
weeping head, grows hot. If his fat were not covered by
hide it would flash into flame. Nothing matters now but
desperate crump and waddle, and the river still
ninety yards away.

The fire, a half mile behind,
the river ninety yards ahead
. . . no odds for a wombat.
He is not an animal to survive
the bush when it thunders this way. Dozens of his koala
cousins have died in the trees. They were not able to move,
of course, but they clung on hard to the branches as the
skin was burned like fresh, wet paint from their
snouts . . . gripped on hard till their hearts were stopped
with smoke . . . and they fell like small, round
torches, lost in the flames.

At first the kangaroo easily outpaced the fire. With a lope of forty miles in an hour he has kept the flames well behind him. The snakes and the koalas die, the dingoes wait their chance, the kangaroo leaps on, and rests, and then takes up again his ancient choreography of limbs and head.

The black smoke thickens in front of his face, and the thunder behind the wombat blots out the noise of the racing fires in the undergrowth. These will reach him first . . . and destroy him. The line of flame spans over thirteen miles, a holocaust that knows nothing of the wombat.

The dingo moves himself to his feet with the shouting flame two hundred yards away. He shakes himself briefly like a dog and then tilts back his head with the action of a wolf. He starts forward, moving easily to meet the fire. And as he moves, his body sinks lower and the paws work harder on the ground giving an athlete's rhythm . . . working harder . . . and then the long, lean head sits low, the body gathers speed with the powerful galloping action of the paws. Seconds before he meets the flames, the dingo reaches cheetah-speed. He plunges through them, eyes shut, head thrust down between the flashing forward legs.

KANGAROOS BURNING
Oil   36 x 48 ins

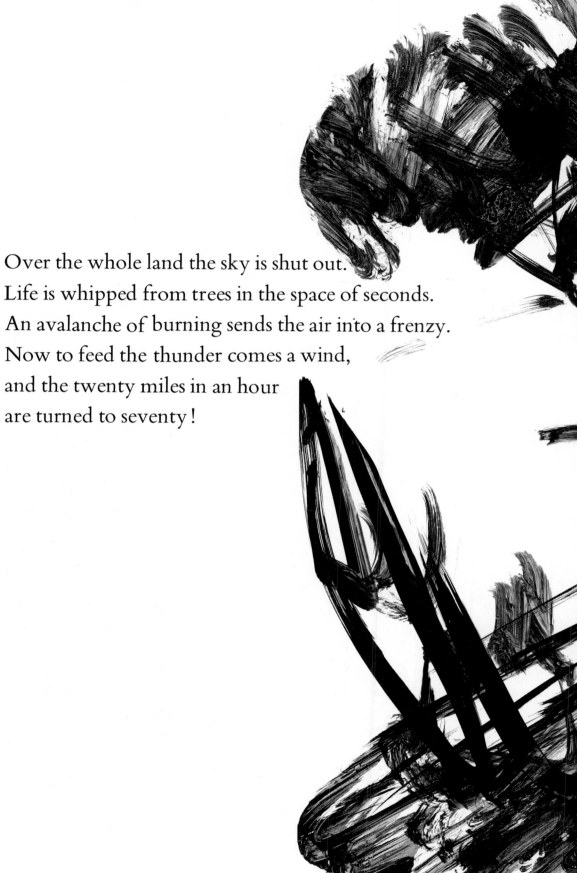

Over the whole land the sky is shut out.
Life is whipped from trees in the space of seconds.
An avalanche of burning sends the air into a frenzy.
Now to feed the thunder comes a wind,
and the twenty miles in an hour
are turned to seventy!

The flames have trapped the
flying kangaroos.
They are tough and they leap with instinct.
Before they die they smell the sweet, strange scent of
roasting flesh. Their mighty paws still strike the ground
while their heads loll downward in death, jerking with
each shudder of the body.
Then the crash, sudden and complete,
no threshing on the ground, with the tiny
heads slewed back
. . . and the flames feed.

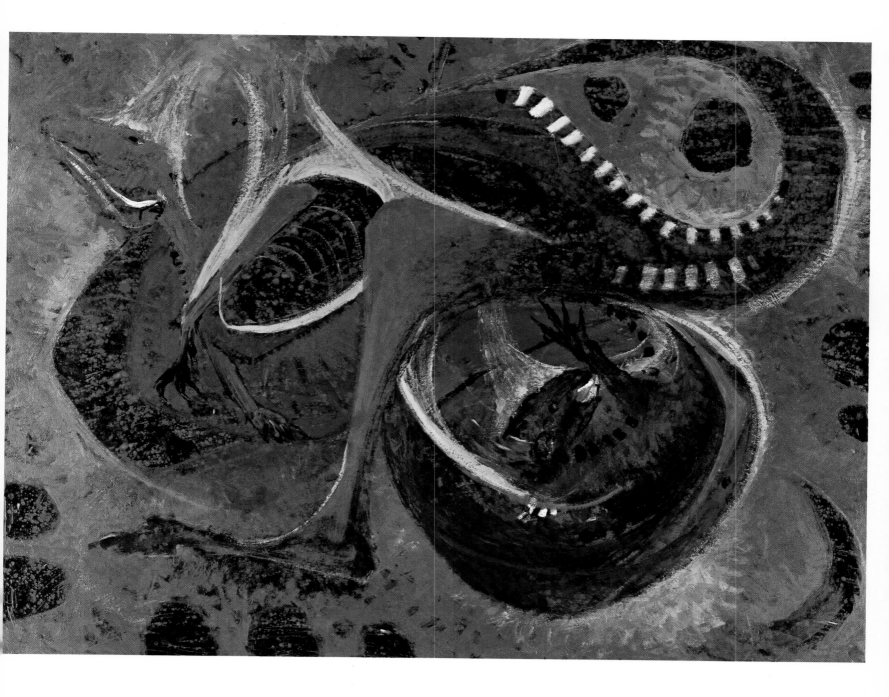

THE FLAMES FEED
Oil   36 x 48 ins

The river is yards ahead of the wombat's snout now, just nine yards. Lurch and crump have sunk to slovenly heave and slide. The flames have washed over him twice, and there are little scrub-fires in his fur. The smoke has made him sob to catch his breath, and the heavy, continual sobbing takes up most of his last strength. His eyes are blind with hot fluid, but his snout detects the river, six yards on. His last fragments of life tell him: there! The flames find him out again. He cries out in blind agony . . . high squealing that doesn't match the lumpy body. He slumps forward. The fire mounts over him. His small shrieks are drowned by the noise. And then, with a capricious change of wind, the fire sweeps back. Soon it is half a mile away.

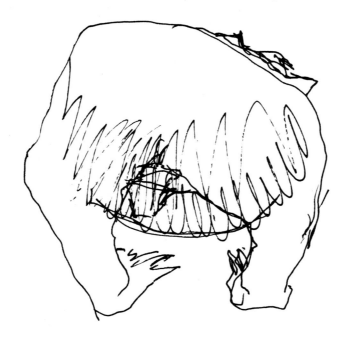

The wombat is left in the smoking bush, undetectable
black among black. Still breathing. Almost dead.
A travesty of wombat. And yet, there is a lurch . . .
waddling will not be possible again and there is no
strength left for crump . . . and another lurch.
He makes the miracle of reaching the river.
Slowly he slides
under water.

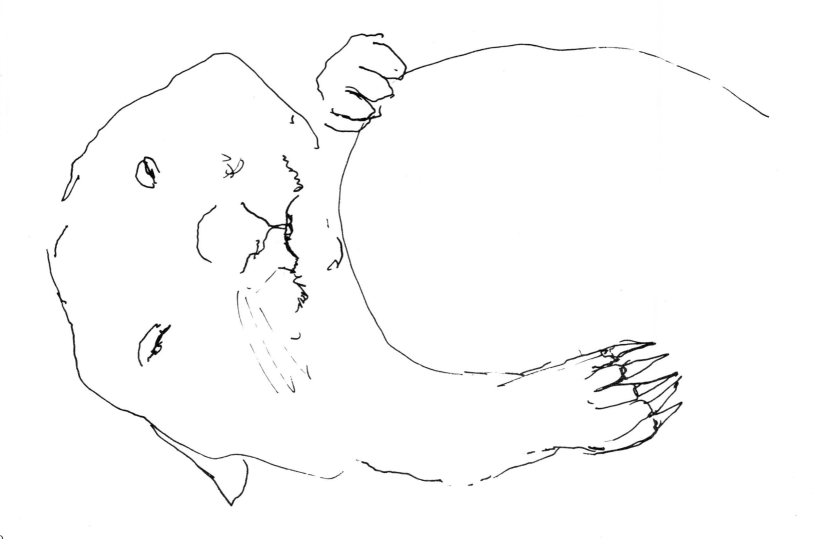

THE DEATH OF A WOMBAT
Oil   36 x 48 ins

A mile away a dingo sleeps,
badly burned but living on.
Closer round, and much further away,
there is death in the forms of
shattered trees, grotesquely twisted kangaroos,
goannas and koalas,
birds and rabbits and snakes.

Nothing
moves,
anywhere.

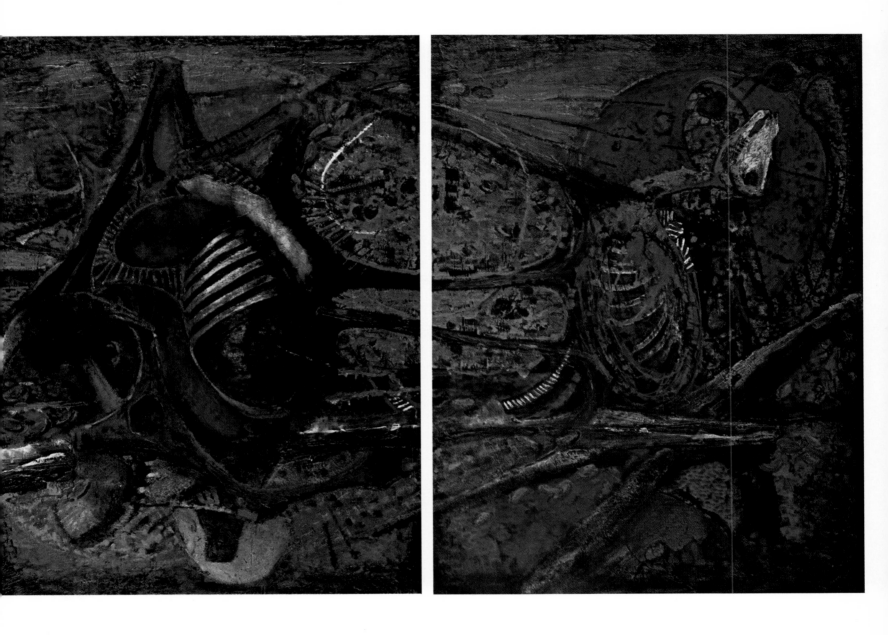

AFTERMATH OF FIRE
Oil.   Triptych 48 x 108 ins

The wombat moves to a soft death now. His fat, charred rump bobs slowly above the water as he drowns. The last thing that he dimly knows is the gentle easing of his terrible burns. A gesture perhaps, to the friend of all the bush, to the meekness of waddle and crump?

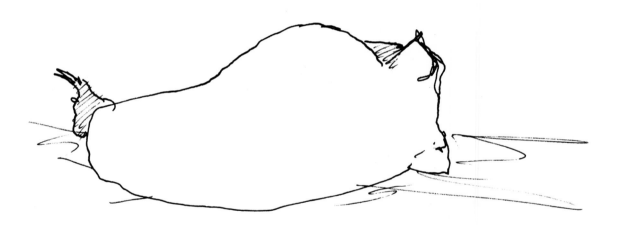

1972

When the sun sets,
the thunder has gone.
The moon comes up.

NEW GROWTH
Oil   36 x 48 ins

Catalogue of Paintings